Cute and Cuddly

Activity Fun Stickers

Written by Brenda Apsley
Designed and illustrated by Sheryl Bone

EGMONT
We bring stories to life

First published in Great Britain 2005 by Egmont Books Limited
239 Kensington High Street, London W8 6SA
This edition published 2011
© 2011 Egmont UK Limited
All rights reserved.
ISBN 978 1 4052 5714 5
53301/1
Printed in China

It's morning, and time for breakfast! Which bowl of milk is for which cute kitten? Color the bowls to match their collars.

Poor Teddy! He's all on his own. Draw and color in a teddy bear friend for him to play with.

Two of these baby lambs are twins. Can you find the 2 that are exactly the same?

Answer: 5 and 9 are exactly the same.

The little goldfish's tank is empty. Draw some plants, shells and pebbles for him – and don't forget to add lots of bubbles.

What a lot of cuddly little bunnies! Can you find the odd one out, and color her in?

Draw lines to give the pets the foods they like to eat.

These pictures tell a story. Finish the pictures by joining the dots, color them in as neatly as you can, and add some stickers if you like.

1

2

Now, tell the story in your own words and decide what you want to call the story.

3

4

Use soft colors to make a new pillow and a patchwork quilt for the baby doll.

Draw and color in your own picture of the lovebirds. It's easy if you do it square by square. Now, write your name on the line.

The Lovebirds by _____

Jess adores her pony! Color in only the 6 things she needs to look after him.

Which pet would you like to have most in the whole world? Draw your dream pet in the outline, and write your name on the line.

My Dream Pet by

These pictures of the pet shop look the same, but 6 things are different in picture 2. Can you spot the differences?

2

Molly is playing doctors and nurses with her toys. Which piece will complete the jigsaw puzzle picture?

Look at these cute puppies! Draw more spots for each puppy to match the numbers on their collars.

This big fluffy cat is very spoiled. No wonder she's called Fussy Cat!
Count the toy mice, collars and bells she has, and circle the right numbers.

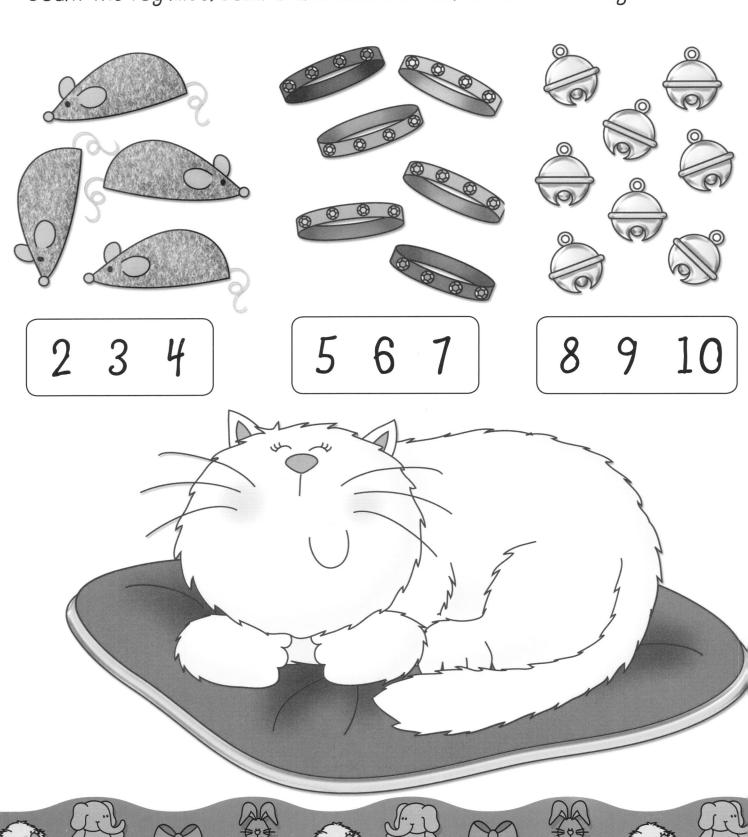

2 3 4

5 6 7

8 9 10

Complete the house by drawing lines between the dots and draw a cuddly pet in it. You could add a sticker too!

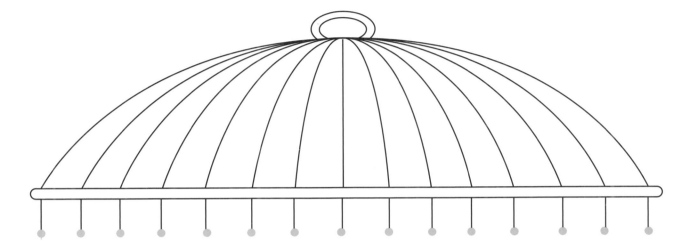

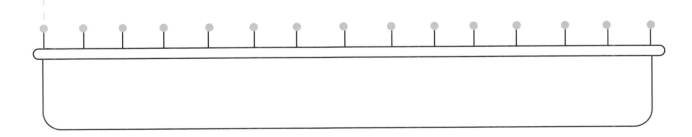

The toys have fun in the playroom when there's no one around! Use the little picture to help you color in the big one.

The little puppy has forgotten where he hid his bones! Can you find 6 for him?

Which kitten is playing with the ball of wool?

Answer: 2

Pretending is fun! Say the name of each animal, make the noise it makes, and do some actions.

woof, woof!

squeak, squeak!

cheep, cheep!

quack, quack!

meow, meow!

The baby doll is so cute! Starting at 1, join the dots to make something extra special for her.

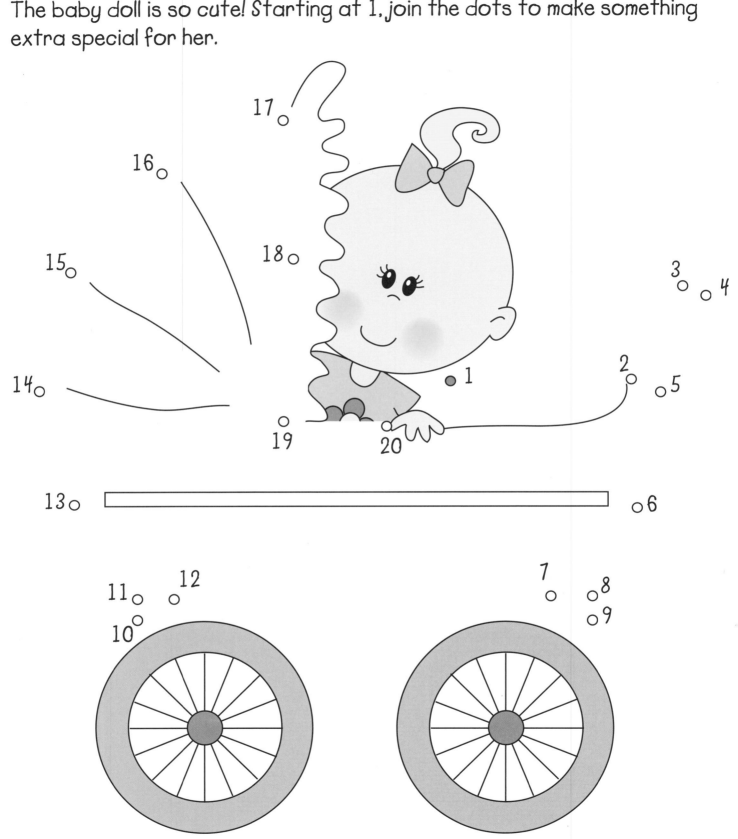

17
16
18
15
3
4
14
2
5
1
19
20
13
6
7
8
12
9
11
10

Which lucky bunny has the most carrots? Which has only 2?

Naughty Ben the pup has been digging in the garden and rolling in the mud!
Read or listen to the story and draw picture 4.

1 "What a mess!" says Sophie. "Woof!" says Ben.

2 Sophie gives Ben a bath, but he doesn't like it. "Woof!"

Now tell the story in your own words. And don't forget to make lots of doggy noises!

3 Then Sophie dries Ben with a big towel.

4 "That's better!" says Sophie. "Woof!" says Ben.

Cheep! The budgie loves talking! Color in the little picture that shows him in his mirror.

1

2

3

The little cygnets want to get back to the mommy swan. Can you show them the way to the pond?

Read or listen to the names of the toys and color them in using the colors on the tins of paint.

Bluey

Blackie

Ginger

Pinky

Which kitten will win the prize in the Most Cuddly Kitten competition? You decide! Write number 1 on the rosette of the kitten you like best, and the numbers 2, 3, 4 and 5 for the others.

The teddy bears are having a picnic. These pictures look the same, but 7 things are different in picture 2. Can you spot the differences?

1

2

Draw lots more cute chicks and cuddly mice to fill the page. Why not add some stickers too?

Draw lines to match the animals to the prints they have made.

Do you know the story of Goldilocks and the Three Bears? Read or listen, then tell the rest of the story in your own words.

1

The Three Bears made some porridge.

2

There was a big bowl for Daddy Bear.

Color in the pictures as neatly as you can, and add stickers if you like.

③ There was a medium-sized bowl for Mommy Bear.

④ Baby Bear had his own tiny bowl. Then along came Goldilocks ...

Color in the elephant with the longest trunk. Now color in the lion with the longest whiskers and the zebra with the longest tail.

Complete the picture of Daisy and her big waggy-tailed dog as neatly as you can.

"Where are you hiding?" says Mommy Bunny. Can you find her 5 naughty babies?

Draw patterns on the cushions to match the kittens and on the balls to match the puppies.

Aren't the little goats cute? Can you find 2 that are exactly the same?

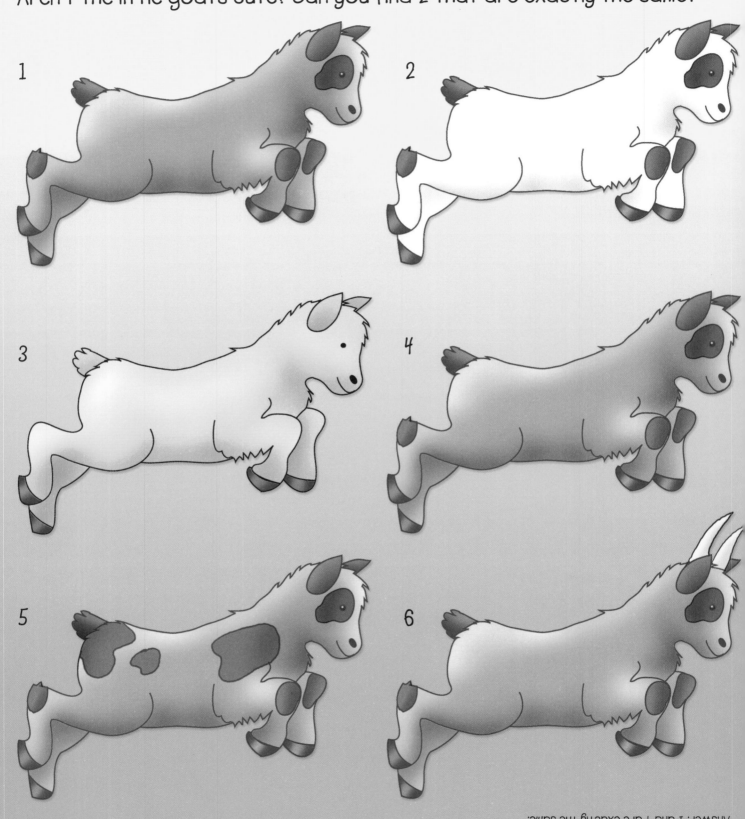

Join the pets to their houses by drawing lines. Do you know what the houses are called?

Which dog is Milly taking for a walk?

Ben

Sam

Tim

What a lot of pretty butterflies! Can you find the odd one out, and color her in?

a

b

c

d

e

f

g

In Sophie's playschool she's the teacher and her toys are the pupils!
Count the number of each thing you can see, and write the numbers down.

1 + 1 =

blocks   teddies   books   crayons

Draw patterns to make new dresses for the baby doll. Which dress do you think she'll like best?

Starting at 1, join the dots to find out who Annie likes to cuddle up to at bedtime. Then color in your picture.